"Cerebus the Aardvark is a brilliant comic. On sheer visual charisma alone, he could blow any other funny animal right out of the water."

Mary-Jo Duffy
EPIC Illustrated

"I think Sim ought to be arrested for pistol-whipping a poor aardvark into having those crazy adventures. Poor aardvark, taken out of the jungle and forced into doing all that weird stuff."

Neil Adams
The Comic Informer

SWORDS OF CEREBUS

Volume Three

Aardvark Vanaheim Inc.

First Printing: Fall, 1981
Second Printing: March, 1984
Third Printing: June, 1985
Fourth Printing: February, 1986

also available:
Swords of Cerebus Vol. 1
Swords of Cerebus Vol. 2
Swords of Cerebus Vol. 4
Swords of Cerebus Vol. 5
Swords of Cerebus Vol. 6

Printed in Canada

ISBN 0-919359-02-7

CEREBUS No. 9 (April - May, 1979)

This issue looks quite a bit different than any of the previous ones -- I don't know if it's as obvious to other people as it is to me (an occupational hazard of being the person who drew it, I've come to realize). There is a very stark quality to the black areas that didn't show up before.

I wish I could say that it was a conscious move on my part to a more graphic and less scratchy style of drawing, but alas, such is not the case. This issue was an experiment in sharing my work-load around to cut down on my drawing time dramatically.

My mouth absolutely begins to water whenever I think of something that might cut down on my drawing time dramatically. And in this case, coincidentally enough, the idea came from Gene Day. Gene around this time had hired his brother Dan to fill in his solid blacks, as well as adding the occasional texture lines, assisting on laying down the tone, erasing inked pages and just generally cutting down on his drawing time dramatically.

I didn't have a brother handy.

But I did have a wife.

Deni liked the idea a whole bunch, since she had wanted from the day I met her to help me out in any way she possibly could (bless her heart). I set to work on the first few pages, pencilling, lettering and then inking in outlines, marking little "x's" on the areas needing solid black and then turning them over to Deni who was also going to lay in the tone as specified.

It was a real vacation.

For a few days.

When the first few pages were done, I was not overly pleased with the way that they looked. I hemmed and hawed and did everything short of accusing Deni of redrawing the stuff behind my back. Being a patient sort, however, I decided that it was strictly a matter of getting used to the style of working and learning how to compensate for what little defects cropped up from time to time.

Things didn't improve.

I was at a complete loss to explain why things worked out better when I did the whole page myself and just didn't look right when someone else filled in the blacks. I mean black is black right? I considered diluting the ink that Deni was using in an attempt to soften the super-stark look before me.

It came as quite a blow when I finally realized what was wrong. I'm a "fixer".

All the way through the inking stage of drawing, I'm adding a little black here, a little black there. Cutting into black areas with white paint, then putting most of it back. Thickening lines and adding texture, putting tone on for a quick look, then stripping it off again and trying something else.

Whatever dreams I may have had of someday owning a studio full of people blacking in areas and pasting in tone were dashed in one moment of realization.

I was on my own.

Looking back on the issue to write this introduction, I am not quite as disheartened by the results. Considering that Deni practically drew the energy globes sequence single-handedly (I went in after and did the white spatter effects) looking at the ratio of black to white on the page, the sequence did not look that much different from what I would have done on my own. But the spotting of blacks on the other pages just could not be accomplished in outline to my satisfaction. It is perhaps worthy of note that Kim Thompson in his review of Cerebus in the Comics Journal found the "marble patterns in the scene with the Panrovian coarse and distracting". I can remember curdling a bit when I saw that page, ashamed to admit that the tonal pattern I had selected did not work at all. Added to my reluctance to ask Deni to pull up all of her hard work and replace it, the whole situation made for a very uncomfortable few weeks.

Moving away from the technical side to the content, you can tell that I very quickly became uncomfortable with Cerebus as Ruler. Here he was with an army of devoted followers and I couldn't wait to ditch them and get him off on his own. I anguished over the decision of how to handle this for some time, aware that the avid Cerebus readers were going to need a plausible explanation of his vacillating approach to leadership. The most obvious quality in his character to latch onto was his competence, combined with his impatience with incompetence. Clearly, he did not have the qualities needed in a leader. It was not quite enough, however, to have him just leave his troops behind and never go back to them. That was when I developed the ending sequence to the story. Cerebus' sudden appreciation of his position and his sudden enthusiasm for an alliance of his own making brings the reader into complete harmony with the story direction.

Cerebus No. 9 (cont'd)

Whatever reservations the reader might have had about the lone wolf being co-opted into a pack are swept aside by the sudden elation of imminent victory and snow-balling success. It was with a great deal of satisfaction that I took Cerebus and the readers on a roller coaster ride of hope for his future and then drew the tracks straight into a brick wall.

For those of you interested in background, Imesh is the city of Cerebus' adolescent years, the place where he studied magic under Magus Doran and first learned how to drink, gamble and raise hell. You can see from the size of the city why it was that Cerebus felt conquest to be a matter of troop strength and dedication to the cause. These northern "cities" are little more than military outposts surrounded by a single wall, Regularly sacked by barbarians or captured in the occasional border raid by a neighbouring tribe. Although this activity is not as wide-spread in the "Aardvarkian Age" as it was in the previous hundred years or so (largely attributable to it being bad for business, and hence frowned on by the emerging merchant class), it is virtually unheard of in the capital cities (like Iest, Beduin, Palnu, etc.) which have remained safe and sound for many years.

The story was also a study in the corrupting influence of power, since (as someone once said) power is not manifest unless it is power **over** some one. Even though my personal feelings about characters like K'cor border on complete revulsion, I still tried to build a certain amount of sympathy for his position and attitudes. Even Ronald Reagen likes puppies, right?

The major point of interest, for me though, was Cerebus' insidious seduction into the game of power itself and its bringing of him to the saddest of all possible points; where there was something to lose.

His first hard lesson in a long string to come.

WAP

HERE! -- *YOU* WEAR THAT CAST-IRON NIGHTSHIRT FOR A FEW HOURS...

BUT, YOUR MAJESTY -- *SURELY*...

AAAG!

OUT OF MY WAY, BISON BREATH!

THE WHOLE LOT OF YOU CAN *FORAGE* FOR GAME AND WATER -- OR UNICORNS AND FAIRY DUST IF YOU WISH...

MEANWHILE, CEREBUS WILL SHOW YOU HOW A *TRUE* WARRIOR TAKES A CITY...

YOUR MAJESTY!

THE CONNIPTINS *ALWAYS* FOLLOW THEIR KING!

STOP!

IF THERE ARE ANY CAPABLE OF FOLLOWING *CEREBUS*...

...THEY ARE WELCOME TO *DO* SO!

CEREBUS WONDERS IF THAT OLD TOAD, **GARSK**, IS STILL CAPTAIN OF THE GUARDS

TARIM! I'VE A FEW OLD SCORES TO SETTLE WITH HIM...

HMM! NO GUARDS ON THE **WALL** ANYWAY! FIRST, CEREBUS WILL HAVE TO FIND SOME TALKATIVE CITIZEN TO WAYLAY...

ONCE I HAVE AN IDEA OF THE TROOP STRENGTH, CEREBUS CAN DECIDE HOW BEST TO TAKE...

unh?

"**TARIM**" MUTTERS THE EARTH PIG "FIRST THE GATE IS MISSING AND NOW IT'S THE WHOLE DAMN **CITY!**" GONE ARE THE WINDING STREETS AND ANCIENT BUILDINGS OF THE AARDVARK'S YOUTH! THE PERIMETER OF THE CITY IS COMPOSED OF CRUDE STONE BUILDINGS WHILE THE CORE IS DOMINATED BY A HUGE ALTAR SWARMING WITH WORKERS AND MASONS! IN POINT OF FACT, THE WHOLE CITY'S ENERGIES SEEM DIRECTED TOWARD THE ALTAR AND THE STRANGE STONE CONSTRUCTION UPON IT...

THEY MUST ALL BE **INSANE!**

NONE BUT **MADMEN** WOULD TEAR DOWN THE RAM AND PEACOCK TAVERN...

WELL -- CEREBUS IS HERE TO CONQUER **IMESH** -- NOT TO MOURN THE PASSING OF ITS HISTORIC **LANDMARKS**...

EVEN SO...

CEREBUS WOULD HAVE GIVEN MUCH TO SEE WHAT SURFACED WHEN THEY DEMOLISHED THE RED CRESCENT QUARTER

CLOVIS' INSTEP! THEY'RE ALL CARRYING STONES! EVERYONE IN THE WHOLE CITY IS BUILDING THAT.... THAT...

TO HELL WITH TROOP STRENGTH -- THE FIRST THING **CEREBUS** HAS TO FIND OUT IS WHAT THESE IDIOTS ARE **BUILDING!**

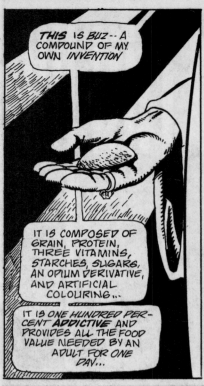

THIS IS *BUZ*-- A COMPOUND OF MY OWN *INVENTION*

IT IS COMPOSED OF GRAIN, PROTEIN, THREE VITAMINS, STARCHES, SUGARS, AN OPIUM DERIVATIVE, AND ARTIFICIAL COLOURING...

IT IS ONE HUNDRED PERCENT *ADDICTIVE* AND PROVIDES ALL THE FOOD VALUE NEEDED BY AN ADULT FOR ONE DAY...

EACH OF MY SLAVES WHO FILLS HIS QUOTA OF ROCKS GETS ONE EACH DAY-- THEY ARE, AS A RESULT, ETERNALLY STUPEFIED AND WELL FED...

NEEDLESS TO ADD, THEIR ADDICTION ALSO MAKES THEM *DILIGENT* WORKERS...

WHEN *IMESH'S* ECONOMY COLLAPSED I GAVE ONE TO EACH MEMBER OF THE COUNCIL OF ELDERS TO GET THEM 'HOOKED'-- THEY GAVE ME THE CITY IN EXCHANGE FOR A YEAR'S SUPPLY...

NOW THAT THEIR SUPPLY HAS RUN OUT, THEY LABOUR WITH THE *REST* OF THE SLAVES!

MY POSITION IS SECURED BY THE FACT THAT SEDRA AND I ARE THE ONLY TWO WHO KNOW THE EXACT *FORMULA* FOR MAKING BUZ...

NOT THAT THERE IS ANY REAL *DANGER* -- MOST OF THE POPULACE HAVE ENOUGH TROUBLE REMEMBERING WHAT DAY IT IS, TO BE CAPABLE OF ORGANIZING A *REVOLUTION*....

WHICH BRINGS US TO *ANOTHER* ISSUE AT HAND, BARBARIAN!

YOU SCALED THE WALL TO MY CITY, DISTURBED *MY* SLAVES, CHASED *MY* FEMALE...

...AND NOW, BY GILASH'S *THIRD EYE*, YOU'RE GOING TO TELL K'COR "WHY"!!

CEREBUS CAME TO *IMESH* FOR ONLY ONE REASON AND THAT WAS TO...

NEVER MIND--I *KNOW* WHY YOU CAME! WE HAVE A *BARBARIAN* COME OVER THE WALL ABOUT TWICE A YEAR! THEY'RE USUALLY IGNORANT NORTH-LANDERS IN SEARCH OF *LOOT*...

ONCE THEY SEE MY SLAVES, THEY CONVINCE THEMSELVES THAT THEY MUST HELP MY SLAVES TO REVOLT-- "TEACH THEM TO *DIE* LIKE MEN"-- WHATEVER *THAT* MEANS...

AYE! K'COR KNOWS YOU BARBARIANS TOO WELL-- WHEN MY SLAVES SHOW NO INTEREST IN REVOLTING, YOU DECIDE THAT YOU WILL AT LEAST TAKE SEDRA TO 'SAFETY' WITH YOU.

BUT, DEAR SEDRA IS NOT INTERESTED, *WITLING!* SHE CHERISHES HER PLACE AT MY SIDE, AND HAS NO INTEREST IN THE WIMS OF *BARBARIANS*...

...ISN'T THAT RIGHT, SEDRA?

YES, BELOVED.

FREEING MY SLAVES--*IDIOCY!* FREE THEM FOR WHAT? SO THEY CAN WANDER THE SNOWS AND STARVE TO DEATH? HERE THEY HAVE LIFE, WARMTH AND *HAPPINESS!*

CEREBUS CAME TO...

I *KNOW* WHAT YOU'RE GOING TO SAY! "THEY ARE MEN AND MEN *SHOULD* BE FREE" A FREEMAN IS DANGEROUS TO HIMSELF AND EVERYONE ELSE. *FREEDOM* SHOULD BE LEFT TO THOSE WHO CAN PUT IT TO GOOD *USE*...

CEREBUS COULD DIE OF OLD AGE WAITING FOR PORKY THERE TO RUN OUT OF WIND...

I USED MY FREEDOM TO GET POWER! AND THEN USED MY POWER TO GET *MORE* POWER...

STILL, AFTER THE CONNIPTINS, IT IS GOOD TO LISTEN TO SOMEONE CEREBUS CAN *UNDERSTAND*.

CEREBUS DOESN'T *LIKE* THIS DESPOT...

BUT CEREBUS AT LEAST *UNDERSTANDS* THIS DESPOT

YOU THINK I CARE NOTHING FOR MY *SLAVES*? DO YOU? MY PEOPLE ARE MY LIFE-- THEY SACRIFICED THEIR FREEDOM FOR A GREATER CAUSE...

AND THAT WOULD *BE*?

THE DEFENSE OF EARTH AGAINST THE *SECRET INVASION OF VENUSIANS!* EVEN NOW, THE SECOND PLANET FROM THE SUN IS MOUNTING IT'S FORCES.

THEY *ARE* COMING!... MAKE NO MISTAKE ABOUT IT!

MAYHAP CEREBUS IS TOO *QUICK* IN SAYING HE UNDER-STANDS THIS *LUNATIC!*

THE STRUCTURE WILL BE TWO HUNDRED FEET HIGH WHEN COMPLETED. IT'S THE SACRED SYMBOL OF THE VENUSIANS, SIGNALLING THE DEATH OF THEIR RACE.

ONE LOOK AT THIS WHEN THEY GET HERE SHOULD PUT A FEW KINKS IN THEIR *PSEUDOPODS!*

HAHAH HAHAHA HAAHAA HAAHA HAKOKO :KAK·AA :COUGH :COUGH:

NOW DO YOU SEE THE IMPORTANCE OF MY MISSION, *INSECT*? IF YOU WERE TO FREE MY SLAVES, THE INVASION WOULD TAKE PLACE *EXACTLY* AS PLANNED...

AND WITH NONE TO RESIST THEM, THEY WOULD SOON HAVE ALL MEN OF EARTH LABOURING IN THE *AMMONIA MINES OF VENUS...*

WAIT! WAIT!

SO FAR AS CEREBUS IS CONCERNED YOU CAN FAST-FRY THOSE SLAVES AND EAT THEM, *CORPULENT ONE*...

I AM KING OF THE NEW CONNIPTIN EMPIRE AND I HAD COME TO IMESH TO CONQUER IT...

AND PERSUADE YOUR MEN TO JOIN MY ARMY! HAVING SEEN YOUR MEN, CEREBUS HAS NO *INTEREST* DRAGGING THEM TO...

EH? WHAT'S *THAT?* A KING YOU SAY? OF COURSE -- OF COURSE! YOUR MEN? YOU ARE A KING WITHOUT *SOLDIERS* THEN?

CEREBUS LEFT THEM FORAGING FOR FOOD AND WATER OUTSIDE YOUR WALLS --

AS THERE SEEMS TO BE NO REASON FOR CEREBUS TO REMAIN HERE, HE WISHES TO...

CAME IN AHEAD OF THEM, *EH?* JUST TO BE SURE! HM! I *LIKE* THAT! A COURAGEOUS KING -- AS I AM A COURAGEOUS *DEMI-GOD!*

WE ARE *ADMIRABLE* FIGURES, YOU AND I!

SO, YOU HAVE COME TO TAKE MY CITY AND MY *SLAVES* FROM ME! VERY WELL -- I AM A FAIR KING -- YOU WILL HAVE YOUR CHANCE TO TAKE MY CITY AND MY SLAVES FOR YOUR OWN! I PROPOSE A WAGER OF KINGS! A *KINGLY* CHALLENGE FOR *KINGLY* STAKES...

IN A FEW MOMENTS, THOSE BARS BEFORE YOU WILL RISE! YOU WILL FOLLOW US INTO THE DOORWAY ON MY RIGHT! IF YOU CAN PASS THROUGH THE CORRIDOR *UNSCATHED* AND THEN DEFEAT MY CHAMPION, YOU WILL WIN MY CITY AND SLAVES! I WILL GIVE YOU ALL THE *BUZ* I HAVE AND SHOW YOU HOW TO MAKE IT.

WITH THAT SECRET YOU WILL CONTROL THEM -- AND IF YOU SO DESIRE...

...THEY WILL CONQUER THE *WORLD* IN YOUR NAME...

IF YOU ARE DEFEATED, YOUR MEN WILL BE WELCOMED TO A *FEAST* BY SEDRA! BY MORNING, MY POOL OF SLAVES WILL HAVE SOME NEW RESERVES...

GOOD LUCK.

DON'T YOU THINK YOU'RE TAKING AN *EXTREME* RISK WITH YOUR..... 'CRUSADE'...?

HAHAHAHAAA! WITH TARIM AND *ANTI-VENUSIANS* EVERYWHERE ON MY SIDE...

I *CANNOT* LOSE...

OF COURSE!

HOW STUPID OF *CEREBUS* TO FORGET...

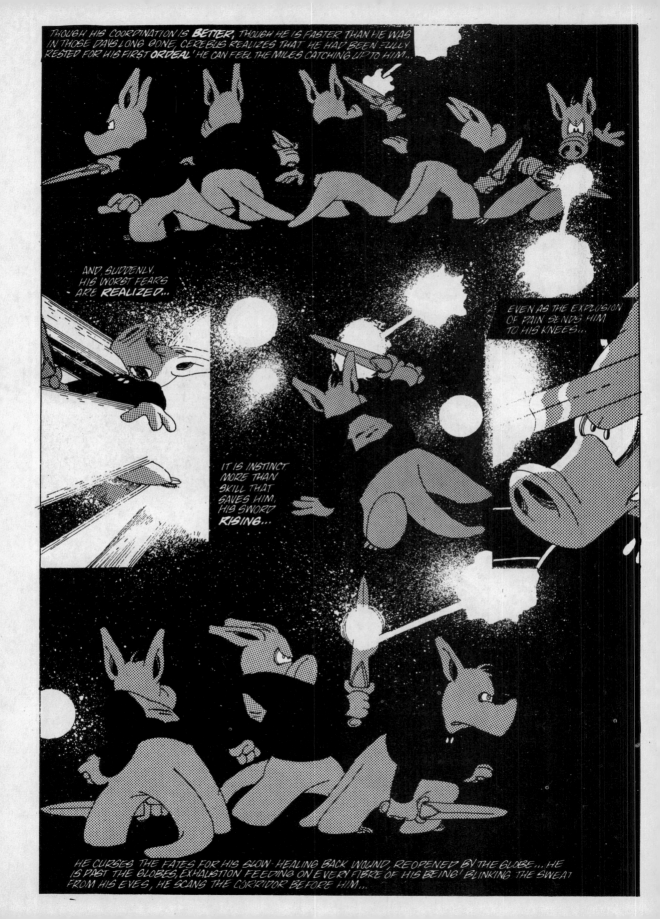

FOR SOMEWHERE UP AHEAD IS K'COR'S CHAMPION, EAGER TO FACE THE EARTH-PIG...

RIGHT NOW, CEREBUS WOULD BE HARD-PRESSED TO BEAT *ELROD* IN HAND-TO-HAND COMBAT...

I AM LORD KOSHEM!...

YOU ARE TO BE *CONGRATULATED* FOR ESCAPING THE GLOBES... BEFORE WE BEGIN, THERE ARE SOME RULES WE MUST...

A PANROVIAN! MAYHAP CEREBUS' LUCK IS CHANGING...

YOUR ACCENT IS NOT *IMESHITE* NOBLE SIR...

NAY! I AM *PANROVIAN,* THE RULES WE WILL...

OH! PANROVIAN, EH? IS IT TRUE THAT PANROVIANS DERIVE SEXUAL SATISFACTION FROM SMALL WOODLAND ANIMALS...?

WHAT?!

CEREBUS HAD HEARD THAT PANROVIAN MEN ARE BUILT SO SMALL THAT *ANYTHING* LARGER THAN A TITMOUSE IS QUITE BEYOND THEIR...uh... *ABILITIES?*

YOUR MAJESTY! I HAVE BEEN SENT TO LOCK SWORDS WITH YOU AND I WOULD HOPE,....

I SAW KING KOREM IN A TAVERN ABOUT A FORTNIGHT GONE...

KING KOREM! TARIM BE PRAISED THAT HE YET...

HE OFFERED TO DRINK THE CONTENTS OF THE *SPITTOON* IF I BOUGHT HIM AN ALE...

CEREBUS THOUGHT THAT WAS A PRETTY GROSS WAY TO MAKE A *LIVING*...

EVEN FOR A *DEGENERATE SOT* LIKE KOREM

CEREBUS HEARD THE PANROVIAN "MARCH OF VIRGINS" HAD TO BE CANCELLED...

...YOUR DAUGHTER GOT *PREGNANT*...

...AND YOUR WIFE REFUSED TO MARCH ALONE...

YOU THINK *PANROVY* IS A JOKE... I... WILL ...*SHOW*... YOU... WHAT... PANROVIANS...

CAN DO!

ACTUALLY, CEREBUS LIKES PANROVIANS

PANROVIANS WILL BE TRUSTED TO DIG LATRINES FOR THE NEW CONNIPTIN EMPIRE

YOU'RE... *EVIL!!!*

PANROVV WILL NEVER BOW TO A TYRANT!...

BUT CEREBUS WISHES TO KNOW MORE ABOUT YOUR *CUSTOMS*...

STOP! STOP!

IS IT TRUE THAT *PANROVIANS* HAVE A LOT OF CHILDREN...

...BECAUSE THEY FIGURE THERE'S ANOTHER *FAMINE* COMING?

NYAHHH

STAND RIGHT *THERE*, OKAY? — DON'T MOVE.

JUST FOR ANOTHER *SECOND!*

THAT'S IT!

AND *NOW*, YOU WORTHLESS GREY TYRANT...

I'M - GOING - TO -

AGLK

SO NOW CEREBUS HAS A CITY FULL OF *DRUG ADDICTS* AND AN ARMY FULL OF *CHEERLEADERS* TO LEAD ON IEST....

IF OUR ENEMIES DON'T LAUGH THEMSELVES SICK, WE MIGHT HAVE A CHANCE...

ALL RIGHT, *K'COR*, CEREBUS HAS ESCAPED YOUR GLOBES AND KILLED YOUR *CHAMPION*...

NOW YOU CAN GIVE ME THE FORMULA FOR BUZ AND CEREBUS WILL...

ONE *MOMENT*, YOUR MAJESTY...

YOU SAY YOU HAVE FACED MY CHAMPION-- YOU HAVE **NOT!** I SAID YOU WOULD HAVE TO PASS THROUGH THE **CORRIDOR**...

AND THEN FACE MY CHAMPION! AS CHAMPION OF MY PEOPLE, I AM CHAMPION, TOO, OF MY OWN **FATE!**

WE HAVE MADE A **WAGER OF KINGS.** BUT I WILL TELL YOU SOMETHING OF KINGS, **YOUR MAJESTY**...

THEIR WAGERS USUALLY BECOME **BATTLES**...

...AND THEIR **BATTLES**...

...**WARS!**

AND **NOW,** WE SHALL SETTLE OUR WAGER...

...AS **KINGS!**

CEREBUS STARES IN STUNNED DISBELIEF AT THE SHINING BLACK ARMOUR BEFORE HIM...

HE CAN FEEL THE ACHE IN HIS LIMBS! THE **THROBBING** THAT BLURS HIS VISION SIGNALS THE ONSET OF **PHYSICAL COLLAPSE**...

'IN A MOMENT, HE REALIZES THE HOPE-LESSNESS OF HIS **SITUATION!** EVEN AT HIS PHYSICAL **PEAK**...

IT WOULD TAKE HOURS TO BEAT AN ARMOURED FOE, HOURS OF **LIGHTNING** THRUSTS AND PINPOINT ACCURACY...

HOURS THE EARTH-PIG'S **RAVAGED** BODY CAN ILL-AFFORD...

THE SLASHING EDGE OF THE **BLACK SWORD** RISES AGAIN AND AGAIN IN THE EARTH PIG'S LINE OF SIGHT...

EACH MOVE IS CALCULATED, **POWERFUL.** "THIS BLUBBEROUS KING", THINKS THE AARDVARK, "IS NO MEAN, "SWORDSMAN."

FACING ALMOST **CERTAIN** DEATH, THE AARDVARK'S BLOWS BEGIN TO GROW LESS ACCURATE...

HE HAS BEEN WITHOUT SLEEP SINCE RISING THE TWO MORNINGS BEFORE AND FRUSTRATION AND DESPAIR EAT AWAY AT HIS SPIRIT...

HE HAD SEEN MEN **FALTER** BEFORE HIM, RECOGNIZING THEIR IMMINENT DEFEAT...

THEY HAD **RECOGNIZED** A HOPELESS SITUATION AS HE DID NOW...

THERE IS A WRIST-TWISTING MOTION THAT **CEREBUS** MISSES AND THE FLAT OF THE SWORD **IMPACTS** SHARPLY WITH THE SIDE OF THE AARDVARK'S HEAD...

REELING **BACKWARD,** CEREBUS MANAGES TO RAISE HIS SWORD TO BLOCK A FATAL BLOW! IN REGAINING HIS BALANCE, HOWEVER ...

...HE IS **UNABLE** TO BLOCK THE RETURN STROKE WHICH RAKES HIS LEFT SIDE, **FRACTURING** ONE OF THE EARTH-PIG'S RIBS...

HE THINKS OF HIS OPPONENT, SWEATING AND PUFFING IN HIS ARMOUR, HIS FLESH **UNMARKED**...

AND AN **IMMENSE** RAGE BOILS UP INSIDE OF CEREBUS,

HE SWINGS **WILDLY**, FEELS THE SWORD CATCH, BRIEFLY, THEN RIP... THERE IS A BLUR OF BLACK, RED AND GREY...

...AND SUDDENLY, K'COR HOLDS THE GREAT BLACK SWORD IN HIS RIGHT HAND...!

A SLOW GRIN CROSSES THE EARTH-PIG'S FACE AND HE **SALUTES** THE GESTURE -- CEREBUS HADN'T DEMANDED HIS OWN ARMOUR...

...K'COR WILL NOT DEMAND COMPENSATION FOR THE WOUND ON HIS HAND...

NOT THAT ANY WOULD BE GIVEN...

CEREBUS SEES THE KING IS **PLAGUED** BY DOUBT-- WONDERING IF CEREBUS COMES TO DO BATTLE -- OR MERELY TO WOUND HIS GOOD ARM...

CEREBUS QUICKLY DECIDES TO LEAVE THE ARM ALONE! THE KING DOESN'T KNOW THAT, HOWEVER AND THE EARTH-PIG ADVANCES...

...SMILING.

IN A WHILE K'COR WOULD DEDUCE THE AARDVARK'S INTENTIONS BUT FOR NOW, CEREBUS RELISHES THE SIGHT OF THE KING, **MINCING** DAINTILY BACKWARDS, SWORD RAISED TO DEFEND HIS ARM...

FEIGNING OUTRAGE AND ANNOYANCE AT THIS OBVIOUS COWARDICE...

CEREBUS DELIVERS A **BONE-RATTLING** BLOW TO THE BLACK-ARMOURED BELLY...

FIGHT, YOU **CORPULENT CRAVEN**...!

CEREBUS HAS CITIES TO **CONQUER**!

K'COR PAUSES, SEEMING TO CONTEMPLATE HIS NEXT MOVE. A MOMENT LATER HIS SHOULDERS SAG WITH RESIGNATION

AND, IN EVIDENT DISGUST, HE FLINGS HIS SWORD AT A WALL BEHIND HIM...

YOU CEDE CEREBUS THE VICTORY, THEN?

GET OUT.

WHAT MANNER OF JEST...?

I POISONED ALL THE WELLS IN THE IMMEDIATE AREA A YEAR AGO TO KEEP BARBARIANS FROM STRAYING TOO CLOSE TO IMESH...

IF YOU DID LEAVE YOUR MEN LOOKING FOR FOOD AND WATER...

THEY ARE ALL QUITE DEAD NOW...

WHICH MEANS YOU ARE NO LONGER OF INTEREST TO ME...

NOW GO!

THE WAGER OF KINGS WAS OVER AS CEREBUS WATCHED THE RETREATING FIGURE OF K'COR...

HE WAS A KING NO LONGER-- WOUNDED, TIRED, HUNGRY

STRANDED WITHOUT FOOD, MONEY OR SHELTER IN A BARREN AND ALIEN LAND...

THE EARTH-PIG'S RAGE AND FRUSTRATION ERUPTS IN A PROTRACTED, PIERCING CRY...

ECHOING AND RE-ECHOING IN UPON ITSELF -- STABBING OUT INTO THE CITY WHERE POWDERY SNOW SWIRLS BETWEEN THE BUILDINGS...

BUT THE IMESHITES, ENGROSSED IN THEIR DAILY CHORES, HEAR NOTHING...

CEREBUS No. 10 (June - July, 1979)

It was time for Red Sophia to return. Elrod had been back once already and hey, fair is fair, y'know. That's about as specious a bit of reasoning as you're likely to hear, but that was the reasoning behind it.

I liked being able to draw the little lady without feeling compelled to copy Barry Smith and Frank Thorne. That was another major consideration in bringing her back for another visit, since I hadn't had a chance to try drawing a female in my own style, which had been developing since issue seven. Besides it was a foregone conclusion that her marriage was not going to work out, being something of a suicidal enterprise for hubby.

Elrod and Red Sophia are very similar characters in their effect on the storyline of Cerebus. They are out of step with the procedings to a large extent, bordering on a schizophrenic disregard for the alternative realities involved. Compare Sophia's entrance in this issue with Elrod's in number seven. In both cases, the captions build a pulpish air of tension, reflecting Cerebus's mood. The reader prepares himself for gut-wrenching adventure right along with the Earth-pig and the grim realities to come, only to find himself in the midst of a grand farce. The question arises in each case of how they got there. We see that Cerebus has ridden long and hard to reach the Temple in number seven and that he has nearly exhausted himself in number ten in the harsh landscape. In comes Elrod on a pair of snowshoes, fit as a fiddle and there's Red Sophia in her chain-mail bikini, barely even aware that the temperature is a might brisk. They are at the opposite end of the spectrum from "accident-prone". They could fall backwards into a pile of shit and come up smelling like a rose.

This was also the first issue, where I consciously built tension between a number of characters by molding four individual points of view at complete odds with all others. Very little actually happens in the story, but I was beginning to lose my compulsion to change locales and situations simply for the sake of variety. Instead I was beginning to emphasize the personalities involved. The relationships between the characters became the priority and the framework. The backgrounds were just backgrounds. It was a minor shift in emphasis, but it was far more in keeping with my own nature; a writer who draws, as opposed to an artist who writes.

This was also the first time that Cerebus is shown to use any discretion whatsoever when it comes to a potential confrontation. It was natural to assume that at some point he would be forced to go a few rounds with the guard. The character is abrasive in the extreme and the reader feels almost cheated that no one takes a poke at the big goon. Practically speaking, however, Cerebus' course of action is the safest and the best in the long run. Discretion is not only the better part of valour, it is the essence of safety.

The situation was also, to a degree, autobiographical. I have never in my life been in a fight, and on a number of occasions, my sense of humour has been what saved me. That and being able to run fast.

This was Red Sophia's last appearance in Cerebus to date. There are a number of reasons for this. Kim Thompson's comment on the "unhealthy origin" of the Marvel character sums up my feelings pretty well. I was initially attracted to the book by Frank Thorne's work, having liked Frank's stuff from the time he was doing Korak and Son of Tomahawk for DC. I heard a great deal about the Sonja Show that he did at conventions and was intrigued by the occasional photograph or write-up one would see in fanzines or on the letters pages. When I first read one of the books, I have to admit to an almost total sense of disgust at the concept behind it. The qualities of sado-masochism, rapist as hero and woman as willing rape victim screamed at me from every panel. I didn't for a moment figure that some fourteen year-old boy was going to go out and defeat his girl-friend in battle for the privileges implied, but it seemed like something less than the ideal structure for an entertainment form.

Sophia was also intended as something of a tribute to Wendy Pini's interpretation of the character in the aforementioned Sonja Show, and finding out that she didn't like the character didn't help matters.

If she does return again, I will have to re-think the concept completely to try and make her at least a little more sympathetic. A gargantuan task that makes me feel I would be better served coming up with a new character altogether.

Those who worry that Red Sophia was another victim of Cerebus' double-cross at the end of this issue can put their minds at rest. Sophia, like Elrod is one of those survivors you

Cerebus No. 10 (cont'd)

just can't keep down for very long.

A major -- scratch that -- THE major development in the artwork took place while I was drawing this issue. I met Marshall Rogers at a Toronto comic book convention for the first time. We had an opportunity to talk at great length about comic books, drawing, materials and much more. While flipping through an issue of Cerebus, he pointed to a panel Cerebus appeared in, indicating the line of an arm. Acknowledging that it looked "okay", he recommended that I try using a Hunt 102 pen nib combined with Windsor-Newton brushes to give it a "beefier" look. To this time, I had been using strictly mechanical pens (Staedler Mars 1.5 and 2) for all of the drawings, using brush only to fill in large areas of solid black. I was extremely reticent, protesting that I had been trying from the first issue to draw Cerebus like an animation cell, with no texture to the lines whatsoever. He politely deflected all my protestations with a characteristic grin (he really does look like the Joker), saying "Try it. Just try it."

He warned me that I wouldn't feel comfortable with the pen for the first while, but gradually I would discover lines that could be drawn with no other weapon.

I started using them on page seventeen and I never stopped.

At first I used them like very skinny, fragile mechanical pens. Gradually I was using the muscles up to my first joint in my index finger -- then the whole finger and a bit of my thumb. Within months I was drawing with my wrist and forearm and if it wasn't for my complete lack of athletic ability, I'd probably be using both legs by now.

Later, it would be Joe Rubinstein who would drive the point home even more with a lesson in contrast of thin and thick lines. Later still I would find out where both of them had gotten the wrist-action fever.

Thank you, Marshall. Thank you, Joe.

And thank you, Dick Giordano, wherever you are.

MERCHANT OF UNSHIB!

IT IS THE SEVENTH DAY OF THE **BLIZZARD!** SINCE IT HAD STRUCK WITHOUT WARNING A WEEK BEFORE, TRAVEL HAD GROUND TO A HALT AND FIVE HUNDRED PEOPLE HAD DIED OF EXPOSURE IN THE IMMEDIATE VICINITY OF IEST

UNAWARE OF THIS, CEREBUS PUSHES RESOLUTELY SOUTHWARD, ASSURING HIMSELF THAT IEST HAS ESCAPED THE POLAR SNOWS AND FREEZING **WINDS...**

HIS LEGS, PISTON-LIKE, CHURN THE POWDER-WHITE SNOW. THE **FOOTPRINTS** SEEM TO GROW FAINTER WITH EACH PASSING MILE, AND AN EMPTY PACK AND **GROWLING** STOMACH SERVE TO REMIND THE EARTH-PIG OF THE URGENCY OF HIS HUNT...

THERE IS A HANDFUL OF SCRAPS IN THE AARDVARK'S PACK. ENOUGH, HE REALIZES TO SUSTAIN HIM FOR PERHAPS HALF A DAY...

THE SNOW HAD DRIVEN MOST OF THE **ANIMALS** TO SHELTER. HIS KILLS HAD BECOME MORE INFREQUENT...

CEREBUS WINCES AS HE LOSES HIS FOOTING AND FEELS THE PAINFUL TUG ON HIS RIBS. THE FRACTURES HAD BEGUN TO HEAL, BUT WERE STILL **SENSITIVE**...

THOUGH DIZZY FROM THE PAIN, HE PRESSES ON... SUCH WAS THE NATURE OF THE STRUGGLE FOR SURVIVAL, *CEREBUS* KNEW...

...THAT OFTEN THE OUTCOME OF THE STRUGGLE WOULD HINGE ON JUST SUCH AN ACHE OR PAIN.

THE FOREST OPENS INTO A SMALL CLEARING AND CEREBUS STRAINS IN A LAST-DITCH EFFORT...

THE CHASE WAS NEARLY OVER AND CEREBUS READIES HIS SWORD ARM FOR....

IT WAS **GONE**. A SMEAR OF BLOOD MARKS THE TERMINATION OF ITS FOOTPRINTS. CEREBUS STOPS, BREATHING HARD...

HIS RIBS ACHE **ABOMINABLY** WITH EACH BREATH, AS HE SCANS THE CLEARING FOR SOME CLUE AS TO THE...

COOCHY-COOCHY-KOO!

AAAK!

SURPRISED YOU, EH? I WAS JUST OUT FOR A STROLL IN THE SNOW AND THIS FINE **JACKRABBIT** CAME HOPPING BY -- YOU LOOK **TERRIBLE**! HOW LONG HAS IT BEEN SINCE YOU'VE EATEN?

I COULD FEEL YOUR RIBS RIGHT THROUGH YOUR SHIRT!

CEREBUS - IS - NOT - GOING - TO FAINT...

ACTUALLY, I'M GLAD I RAN INTO YOU THIS WAY -- I'VE GOT SOMETHING TO **TALK** TO YOU ABOUT...

HOWZABOUT I FRY UP A QUICK BATCH OF BUNNY BURGERS AND THEN WE CAN...

CEREBUS HAS NO ...INTEREST IN SUCH SMALL GAME.

GREAT-- THEN WE'LL JUST GO TO MY TENT AND *TALK*...

CEREBUS HAS NOTHING TO SAY TO YOU...

UNFORTUNATE, BUT-- SOPHIA HAS SOMETHING TO SAY TO *YOU*!

uh-- DOES THE *BLACK BLOSSOM LOTUS* MEAN ANYTHING TO YOU?

SO YOU FOUND A FRAGMENT, EH? *CEREBUS* IS NOT IMPRESSED.

BESIDES-- THERE HASN'T BEEN AN *AUTHENTIC* FRAGMENT DISCOVERED IN NEARLY FIFTY YEARS...

THE ONE I HAVE MY EYE ON ISN'T A *FRAGMENT,* DEAR HEART...

IT'S *INTACT.*

MY TENT IS THIS WAY...

BUNNY BURGERS ...

YECH!

I'VE BEEN SAVING THIS BOTTLE OF DEHRSION BUBBLY FOR A SPECIAL OCCASION AND THIS IS...

CEREBUS?

UNH!

IN THE LAST WEEK, CEREBUS HAS HAD HIS BACK BLASTED, HIS RIBS FRACTURED AND HIS *EMPIRE* SLIPPED OUT FROM UNDER HIM BY A BLIMP IN BLACK ARMOUR. HE HASN'T EATEN OR SLEPT SINCE YESTERDAY AND WHAT LITTLE PATIENCE HE HAS IS WEARING *QUITE* THIN!

NOW! EITHER YOU TELL CEREBUS WHERE TO FIND *THE BLACK BLOSSOM LOTUS* OR HE'LL...

OOOH--YES! YES! DO IT *HARDER*, MY DARLING! YOU *SWEETHEART*, YOU! HOW DID YOU GUESS THAT I'M INTO BEING DOMINATED?

ALL RIGHT! CEREBUS KNOWS WHEN HE'S BEATEN! *KEEP* THE LOTUS FOR YOURSELF. CEREBUS HAS *HAD* IT!

DON'T *BE* THAT WAY, *DARLING*-- I'LL TELL YOU *ALL* ABOUT THE LOTUS-- BUT DON'T YOU THINK YOU COULD BE A *TEENSY* BIT NICER TO ME? IT'S BEEN *SO* LONG SINCE I'VE BEEN IN A MAN'S ARMS...

CEREBUS ISN'T A MAN...

CEREBUS IS AN *AARDVARK!*

WHAT TREACHERY IS THIS, THEN?

A SCUM-SUCKING SAWED-OFF KHAIVEN! YOU CAN'T TAKE OVER OUR COUNTRY BY FORCE, SO YOU HOUND US IN OTHER LANDS!

CEREBUS-- THIS IS MEIRGEN... HE GETS THE THIRD SHARE.

MEIRGEN-- SAY HELLO TO CEREBUS THE AARDVARK...

I'LL FEED YOUR HEART TO THE WOLVES, YOU STINKING KHAIVEN SCUM!

AND YOU, SOPHIA-- SENDING MEIRGEN OUT TO CHECK THE CARAVAN-- WHILE YOU... LINGER... HERE WITH THAT-- THAT SCUM-SUCKING...

"...SAWED-OFF KHAIVEN." I HEARD YOU THE FIRST TIME.

SMAT

SORRY I DIDN'T WARN YOU THAT WE HAD **COMPANY** COMING

NOT AT ALL--**CEREBUS** IS GETTING USED TO BEATING UP COMPLETE STRANGERS WHENEVER YOU'RE AROUND...

TCAPMIN ISN'T HE?

YOU HAVE A KEEN EYE FOR **CRAZIES!** HE'S THE SON OF THE **JEWELLER** I TOLD YOU ABOUT. WHEN THE MERCHANT BOUGHT HIS LATE FATHER'S **LOTUS**, HE GOT SUSPICIOUS-- DECIDED TO FIND OUT WHAT HE HAD **SOLD**.

I PROMISED HIM "SPECIAL FAVOURS" IF HE SPLIT THE PROFITS WITH ME...

CEREBUS THOUGHT YOUR "SPECIAL FAVOURS" WERE ONLY FOR THOSE WHO DEFEATED YOU IN BATTLE.

YOU'RE NOT **LISTENING!** -- I SAID THAT I **PROMISED** HIM "SPECIAL FAVOURS"...

I SAID **NOTHING** ABOUT ACTUALLY, uh, "FAVOURING" HIM...

DO YOU WANT **CEREBUS** TO REVIVE HIM?

MMM. BETTER LEAVE THAT TO **ME**...

HE'S APT TO BE A BIT **TESTY** WHEN HE WAKES UP.

WELL, I GUESS NOW I HAVE TO BRIBE YOU. JOIN US AND WE'LL GIVE YOU A FULL SHARE -- *TEN-GOLD-PIECES!*

THE GUARD, WHO HAD *ALREADY* SOLD HIS LOYALTIES FOR EIGHT COPPER COINS, PAUSES AND HIS BROW DEVELOPS DEEP FURROWS.

IT WOULD MEAN LESS MONEY PER SHARE, BUT *CEREBUS* DID NOT RELISH THE IDEA OF QUARRELING WITH THE *TCAPMIN...*

THE BORDER GUARDS WERE KNOWN FOR THEIR HAIR-TRIGGER REFLEXES AND *TEMPERS...*

A SLOW GRIN SPLITS THE FEATURES OF THE GRIM BLONDE *NORTHLANDER*

TELL ME YOUR PLAN! IF I THINK IT WILL WORK I WILL JOIN.

OKAY! THIS IS OUR ONLY CHANCE TO KEEP A SHARE OF THE *LOTUS!* MAKE IT A GOOD PLAN...

CEREBUS THOUGHT YOU *HAD* A PLAN!

I *HAD* PLANNED TO TAKE THE GUARDS BY SURPRISE AND OVERPOWER THEM WHILE THEY SLEPT...

SOMEHOW I DON'T THINK HE'LL HAVE TOO MUCH *FAITH* IN THAT IDEA...

WELL?

LET'S HEAR YOUR *DAMN* PLAN!

HOWEVER, I THINK THAT WE SHOULD GET SOME *BUSINESS* OUT OF THE WAY, FIRST.

SINCE THIS CROSSBOW MAKES ME THE MOST *IMPORTANT* MEMBER OF THE GROUP, I THINK I SHOULD GET *TWO* SHARES-- *TWENTY* GOLD PIECES.

BUT THE LOTUS WAS *MY FATHER'S*, AND YOU'RE ALLOWING LESS THAN SEVEN GOLD PIECES FOR EACH OF US! THAT'S COMPLETELY *UNACCEPTABLE!*

SOPHIA COULD MAKE MORE THAN *THAT* SELLING HER OLD CHAIN MAIL BIKINIS TO PERVERTS IN *IEST*...

IF YOU *PREFER* I CAN CALL OUT FOR SOME *ASSISTANCE*...

AND YOU'LL BE *DEAD* WHERE YOU STAND!

CEREBUS IS GETTING *TIRED* OF SAYING THIS...

...BUT HE KNOWS WHEN HE'S *BEATEN*.

LET'S GO FIND A *BRIDGE*.

AMAZING HOW SOME THINGS ONLY MAKE SENSE WHEN YOU HAVE SOMEONE *EXPLAIN* THEM TO YOU.

ISN'T IT THOUGH?

ARE YOU *CRAZY* OR JUST PLAIN *STUPID?* HE'S A *TWENTY-YEAR-MAN!* CEREBUS COULD UNDERSTAND IF YOUR *LIFE* DEPENDED ON...

CEREBUS -- A MAN HAS TO *DO* WHAT A MAN HAS TO *DO* --

THAT'S VERY *GOOD!* DID *SOMEONE* MAKE IT UP FOR YOU OR ARE YOU JUST *CLEVER* WITH WORDS?

AND RIGHT NOW WHAT *I* HAVE TO DO IS...

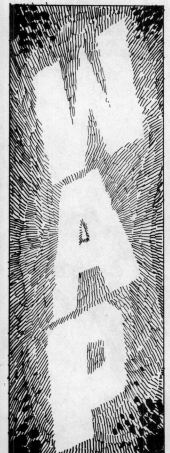

GET YOUR FACE *PUNCHED?*

NO, NO NO...

WHAT I WAS ABOUT TO SAY WAS...

RIGHT NOW, WHAT *I* HAVE TO DO IS...

...GET YOUR *RIBS* KICKED?

JUST ... ONE ... MORE TRY...

I THINK I'M ..... GETTING THE HANG OF IT...

...TELL YOU *WHAT*...

HOW ABOUT *YOU* GET SOPHIA *TODAY*... AND I GET HER *TOMORROW*!

HOW ABOUT YOU DRAG YOUR BLOODY CARCASS *AWAY* FROM HERE...

...BEFORE I *VENTILATE* YOUR WINDPIPE. HMM?

NEVER LET IT BE SAID THAT *MEIRGEN OF RESS* TURNED DOWN A *COMPROMISE*...

CEREBUS WOULD LIKE TO *BORROW* YOUR FUR -- IT IS GOING TO BE COLD TONIGHT AND HE CAN USE IT FOR A TENT...

HA! A *TENT!* DID YOU HEAR *THAT,* SOPHIA? HE WANTS TO USE MY FUR FOR A *TENT!* YOU SURE HAVE SOME *FUNNY* FRIENDS...

CEREBUS? OH, YES -- HE'S A LAUGH-A-MINUTE

I GUESS.

SOPHIA SMILES AT THE EARTH-PIG IN GRATITUDE. SHE HAD EXPECTED A FIT OF JEALOUS RAGE NOW THAT HE WAS NO LONGER HER *TRUE LOVE*...

FOR *ONCE,* THOUGH, SHE HAD ALLIED HERSELF WITH A *WINNER!* HENROT, FERAS AND ALL THE OTHERS WERE BEHIND HER NOW...

GOOD LUCK, *CEREBUS*...

BE *CAREFUL* THEY DON'T SEE YOU...

AND SO, THE EARTH-PIG DEPARTS, LEAVING SOPHIA TO HER DREAMS OF SUNKEN MARBLE BATH TUBS AND MALE ATTENDANTS...

...THE TCADMIN TO HIS DREAMS OF GOLD AND SOPHIA...

...AND MEIRGEN TO HIS DREAMS OF RIBS THAT DIDN'T *HURT* QUITE SO MUCH!

HELLO-- I'M *CEREBUS THE AARDVARK.* YOU HAVE EXACTLY FOUR SECONDS TO HAND OVER THE *BLACK BLOSSOM LOTUS...*

AND YOU'VE JUST USED UP *THREE* OF THEM...

HAVE A NICE TRIP BACK TO *UNSHIB...*

NOW, IF CEREBUS COULD ONLY SEE THE LOOK ON *THROGO'S* FACE WHEN HIS COMRADES SWOOP DOWN ON HIM...

...IT WOULDN'T BE A HALF-BAD DAY...

CEREBUS No. 11 (August - September, 1979)

Marshall Rogers again.

Same convention. Same conversation. Except this time the topic of conversation wasn't materials or techniques. This time the subject was Batman. Excuse me -- THE Batman.

There is perhaps no bigger The Batman fanatic than Marshall Rogers. He also has his own singular view of how the character should be handled and no other way quite measures up. Marshall Rogers talking about The Batman, projecting this gut-wrenching motivation he sees in the Bruce Wayne/Batman split personality is as nice a piece of theatre as you're likely to find at a comic book convention.

Simply put, he sees the Batman as a sicko -- off the deep end. This otherwise normal millionaire who every night starts to slowly metamorphose into this deeply disturbed Figure of the Night. There's a part of him that doesn't want to put the costume on and go out in that damn rain and wind, but it's, like, the costume keeps screaming "put me on! put me on! You're The Batman." Once the costume is on, he's not even vaguely human in disposition. Every evil-doer becomes Joe Chill and the demon has to be excorcised. All these years and every night, he has to relive that horrible moment when Joe Chill stepped from the shadows and .... You get the idea.

Heady stuff, indeed.

It started me thinking about the whole basis of The Batman Legend. Marshall talks jokingly about doing a treasury sized team-up between The Batman and Captain America. The Batman slinking around alleyways, shoulders hunched, shadows everywhere, and his cape up over his face. Hsss. And here comes Cap bounding along, all red white and blue; the neon sign of super-heroes -- about as innocuous as the Macy's Parade coming through your bathroom.

And it's true. Batman -- heh heh sorry -- The Batman is the perfect counterpoint to Superman and the boys. They would clean up a crime, but stick around to sign a few autographs, kiss a few babies. Make nice on the good people. The Batman didn't want anyone to know he was there. Break their heads, kick a few asses and then get away before anybody shows up with (gaahh) strong lights, flashbulbs. Dark. Find some dark and curl up in it. Wrap your cape around you. And keep your eyes peeled for any of those murderous, thieving scum that might happen along.

Hsss.

Once I had that, the story just about wrote itself. The biggest problem was trying not to do it too literally. No kidding. By the time I had seen the Sarah Bernhardt of comics do three performances (last complete show: 1:00 a.m.) I was just about ready to do an all-drama issue of Cerebus. That was when I started adding a few of my own touches. I started wondering "What if Bruce Wayne is a nutbar too?" What if he didn't remember being The Batman. He just woke up every day and there was another twenty grand in a pile at the foot of the bed. Gold teeth ripped from criminal mouths, negotiable bonds from a jay-walking industrialist. I mean if you're going to kick ass, why not turn a profit? Hm?

Hsss.

The "hsss" by the way is a direct steal from Jules Feiffer's Hostileman that appeared in Playboy, a strip I consider one of the best essays on super-heroes ever written. It fit The Batman to a "t".

It was with the greatest sense of great that I realized I wouldn't be able to use the name. It had become such an integral part of the whole concept, that I felt cast adrift. I finally opted for the most disgusting critter I could think of. I even had an origin sequence in mind that had to be scrapped because of space limitations (you'll notice that the story is a wee bit crammed in). "Hss. Criminals are a superstitious and cowardly lot, so my disguise must make them toss their cookies." Cockroach crawls across his sandwich. Gluckkkk. "That's it! A cockroach ... I'll be a Cockroach."

Hsss.

This issue marked a major turning point in a number of ways.

Although I still hadn't mastered it, the pen and brush were already adding a new dimension to the pages. I always wondered how Berni Wrightson got those wood grains so thin.

It was also the first big city that Cerebus had ventured into in the series (lest in No 6, but he stuck mostly to the lower class areas that were essentially the same as the cities of his youth). The merchant takes him into the nicer areas (against his nature, as seen by page one) and circumstances keep him there. His resourcefulness takes a turn for the better, as he runs his first scam of any great proportion, realizing that you can get anyone to do anything if you just push the right buttons. He doesn't realize of course that it's a long road to travel, as seen by

Cerebus No. 11 (cont'd)

the trouble he gets into in later issues with his cleverness. there is a recurring theme to these manipulations; it's not what the aardvark says, it's how he says it. Even though the Cochroach doesn't know what a condominium is, he is an instant convert to the cause. It takes a very strong and secure personality to say no to Cerebus when he's in top form.

It also established the personality of The Cockroach that would remain through his other appearances. He needs someone to pull the strings; whether it's Cerebus, President Weisshaupt, or Astoria. His freelancing days ended when he found the cause he was looking for; raising up the poor and helping them to live like good and decent folk. He and Green Arrow would get along fine.

The first introduction I wrote for this story was a lengthy dissertation on the nervous breakdown I suffered after this issue was finished. It ran to about twice the length of this one, at least, but in the end, it sounded like what it was; a self-serving rationalization of a very insane couple of weeks. I realized when I had it done, that my intention had been primarily to reassure everyone reading it that it wouldn't happen again. Including me. It was the culmination of many different threads in my life coming together at once. Personal stuff, professional stuff, problems, ambitions, accomplishments and failures. Writing that introduction was a very therapeutic exercise, but the final product was pretty dull.

When Kevin Davies of MIRIAD did the interview with me, he asked me if I could have avoided the nervous breakdown, a question I really didn't consider too extensively until I saw it again in print. I don't think I could have, and in many ways, it came at exactly the right time. It was a warning that I am only human and it was an indication to me of just how fragile human can be. I've learned to accept only as much pressure as I can comfortably handle, and to keep my own feelings as the primary focus for my decision-making. Talking to people like Wendy Pini, I began to realize that the people attracted to success (and success is the honey for a specific kind of fly) can bleed you white if you let them, all with the best of intentions.

I realized writing the introduction that I was trying to help anyone who might find themselves in the same situation I did. I was hoping in some way to reach anyone who might be feeling themselves losing control -- babbling endlessly about nothing, swinging from elation to depression and back in a matter of minutes. Unfortunately, it's a pit that you either climb out of or slip into permanently. But the answers have to come from inside.

Enthusing about Marshall Rogers, The Batman, and the pleasure I can get out of a steel point barely a half-inch in length and a bottle of ink, rather than rehashing a dead end period of my life, is one of those answers.

For me.

THE MERCHANT THE COCKROACH

CEREBUS HARBOURED THE BELIEF THAT BEDUIN EPITOMIZED THE **WORST** ASPECTS OF LOWER FELDA. ONLY *IN* **BEDUIN** COULD YOU DEBATE *PHILOSOPHY* WITH A SOLDIER BY DAY...

AND BY NIGHT, AWAKE TO FIND HIM CARVING A NEW MOUTH UNDER YOUR CHIN...THE CITY ALSO FAIRLY **REEKED** OF WINE AND PERFUME...

HE ALMOST WISHED HIS COMPANION **WAS** LEADING HIM INTO A **TRAP** SO HE COULD VENT HIS RAGE! BUT FIRST HE HAD TO SEE IF THE MERCHANT WAS SERIOUS ABOUT THE **HUNDRED** GOLD COINS...

I HOPE FOR BOTH OUR SAKES THAT YOU HAVEN'T *STUMBLED* ACROSS A *FAKE.* IN THE PAST WEEK ALONE I'VE BOUGHT MEALS FOR A *DOZEN* BAR PATRONS CLAIMING TO POSSESS *AUTHENTIC* MAGIC CHARMS

I'VE TOYED WITH THE IDEA OF OPENING A SPARE PARTS CLINIC FOR *LIZARDS, BATS* AND *RABBITS*...

WHY DO YOU KEEP LOOKING *AROUND*?

THERE HAVE BEEN A NUMBER OF INCIDENTS OF *VIOLENCE* IN THIS NEIGHBOURHOOD.'A MERCHANT MUST BE *CONSTANTLY* ON HIS GUARD...

CEREBUS HAS YET TO MEET A MAN WHO *DIDN'T*...

HA HA! MERCHANT OR *OTHERWISE,* EH? WELL *PUT* MY *DIMINUTIVE* FRIEND...THESE *ARE* BIZARRE TIMES...

BUT, *NOW*...

I SHOULD LIKE TO SEE YOUR 'LOTUS'...

AYE! IT IS THE *LOTUS* -- AND A BARGAIN AT A *HUNDRED GOLD PIECES!* PROBABLY THE PUREST MAGIC OBJECT IN THE KNOWN WORLD.

THERE IS BUT *ONE* THING CAN BE DONE WITH IT...

CEREBUS IS A **BUSINESSMAN** HIMSELF...

FROM TIME TO TIME...

AH, YES! THE MONEY!

YOU CAN **COUNT** IT IF YOU LIKE.

NO NEED.

IF THERE ARE ANY COINS **MISSING**...

CEREBUS WILL RETURN AND **DIVEST** YOU OF CERTAIN CRITICAL PORTIONS OF YOUR **ANATOMY**...

YOU'LL WANT TO SAVE SOME **RAGE** FOR MY ACCOUNTANT... HE'S THE ONE WHO FILLS THE SACKS...

BEDUIN IS A **CESSPOOL** OF DEGENERATES AND CUTTHROATS IN POWDERED WIGS...

CEREBUS WOULD NOT LIVE HERE IF THE REST OF THE WORLD TURNED TO **ORANGE SLIME!**

YOUR PHRASEOLOGY LEAVES SOMETHING TO BE **DESIRED,** BUT I TAKE IT YOU ARE OFFERING ME SOME *"FRIENDLY ADVICE!"* MAYHAP =YAAAWN= WE CAN DISCUSS THE MERITS OF **BEDUIN** ANOTHER TIME...

CEREBUS WAS **JUST** LEAVING...

CEREBUS OWED HIM SOME ADVICE FOR BUYING THE *LOTUS,* BUT IF HE'S GOING TO ...

MMBLE MM GRABLEM KILL 'EM ALL! HSSS! BREAK 'EM IN TWO!

I'M MMBLE KILL EVERY ONE OF 'EM! HSSS.

YOU WON'T ESCAPE, MURDERERS!

I'LL BREAK YOUR SPINES AND STOMP ON YOUR FACES mm

DO YOU **HEAR** ME?!!

I'M GOING TO KILL YOU *ALL!*

HSSS.

CEREBUS IS JUST GOING TO **WALK AWAY.** WHAT IS GOING ON IS OF **NO** CONCERN TO CEREBUS

CEREBUS HAS HIS GOLD AND CEREBUS IS NOT GOING TO FALL FOR ANY STUPID *TRICKS...*

CEREBUS IS GOING INTO THE FIRST TAVERN HE COMES TO AND...

ON THE **OTHER** HAND, ONE QUICK LOOK AND CEREBUS WILL LIKELY SEE THERE IS A **LOGICAL** EXPLANATION FOR ALL OF THIS...

EVIL! EVIL! EVIL!

HSSSS!

THEN *AGAIN...*

CEREBUS DOESN'T *GET* IT...

SLINK-- *LURK!*

HE BEAT UP THE GUY WHO KILLED HIS PARENTS AND EVEN GOT A POUCH OF GOLD TO HELP *CONSOLE* HIMSELF.

SHADOWS! SHADOWS! HEE-HEE!

REVENGE! REVENGE!

SO WHAT'S HE AFTER *NOW?*

THERE'S ONLY *ONE* THING MORE IDIOTIC THAN RUNNING AROUND IN A MASK AFTER DARK IN A *SNOWSTORM*...

AND THAT'S *FOLLOWING* SOMEONE IN A MASK AFTER DARK...

...ONE FLIGHT UP ON AN *ICE-COVERED* LEDGE...

HEE-HEE! PUNCH 'EM INNA FACE!

KICK 'EM INNA *STOMACH* ≡ giggle ≡

...AND THAT GOES FOR YOUR LITTLE *DOG*, TOO! HEEHEEHEE!

HALT, KILLER!

ANOTHER KILLER?

MY PARENTS--*DEAD*--AND IT'S ALL *YOUR FAULT*-- NO LOVE-- NO ONE TO WIPE MY NOSE AND KISS ME ON THE NOSE AT NIGHT-- IT'S NOT *EASY* LOSING YOUR MOTHER AT NINETEEN

I--I THAT'S EASY FOR *YOU* TO SAY!

I'VE BEEN ALL ≡SOB≡ ALONE EVER SINCE *YOU*, YOU RED CLAW FOLLOWERS... KILLED MY MOM AND DAD! *THIRTY YEARS*...

THIRTY ≡SOB≡ YEARS!

THIRTY YEARS?

THIS NUT HAS BEEN RUNNING AROUND IN A BUG SUIT...

FOR *THIRTY* YEARS?!!

NO WONDER HE CAN AFFORD TO PAY *ONE HUNDRED GOLD PIECES* FOR HIS *FISHBAT*...

A GOOD NIGHT'S WORK! MAYHAP ONE DAY I WILL SEE A TIME WHEN *ALL* IS GOOD AND JUST AND *COCKROACH-Y* BUT FOR NOW, I NEED REST...

YOU HEAR ME, *RED CLAW BUTCHERS?* THERE ISN'T A HOLE BIG ENOUGH FOR YOU TO HIDE FROM...

...THE *WRATH OF*...

...*THE COCKROACH!* HSSS!

CEREBUS ONLY HOPES THIS *SOLILOQUY* LASTS UNTIL I BEAT HIM *HOME!*

WITH CEREBUS' LUCK, SOMEONE STOPPED HIM TO ASK DIRECTIONS...

...IN WHICH CASE HE WON'T BE HERE FOR *DAYS!*

ONCE MORE I RETURN TO MY SECRET *ROACH LAIR!* HSSS!

AHA!

RETURN OF THE COOTIE!

HM. A CONCEALED PANEL... LOOKS LIKE CEREBUS WILL HAVE NO TROUBLE ADDING A COUPLE OF PURSES TO HIS *EARNINGS...*

SLEEP. MUST... SLEEP.

MOMENTS LATER, HIS COSTUME SECRETED BEHIND ANOTHER PANEL, THE *MERCHANT* COLLAPSES INTO A CHAIR...

REVENGE

REVENGE

MMM...

IF *CEREBUS* IS GOING TO FOLLOW LUNATICS THROUGH THE SNOW...

...HE'S GOING TO MAKE SURE HE DOESN'T DO IT FOR *FREE...*

"WHAT? WHAT'S THIS?"

OH YES *"JUST LEAVING"*. WELL THANK YOU FOR THE *LOTUS*. WE'LL TALK ABOUT BEDUIN SOME *OTHER* TIME! REALLY MUST GET SOME *SLEEP...*

CEREBUS-- UH-- THAT IS...

GOOD NIGHT.

SOMEHOW, THE MERCHANT AND THE COCKROACH ARE *TWO* PEOPLE IN *ONE* BODY! WHEN CEREBUS LEFT THE *FIRST* TIME, THE MERCHANT FELL ASLEEP AND THE COCKROACH WOKE UP. WHEN THE *COCKROACH* FELL ASLEEP, THE MERCHANT WOKE UP UNAWARE OF WHAT THE COCKROACH HAD BEEN *DOING...*

WHICH MEANS THE *MERCHANT* DOESN'T KNOW THAT THERE ARE TWO PURSES HIDDEN IN THAT SECRET PANEL...

CEREBUS HAD BETTER GET THOSE TWO PURSES, BEFORE THE *COOTIE* WAKES UP...

...AND SPENDS THEM ON *ANTENNA POLISH* OR SOMETHING...

CEREBUS SHOULD *PROBABLY* LEAVE THE GOLD OUTSIDE WITH HIS *SWORD*...

BUT HE IS TAKING NO CHANCES OF LOSING THE ONLY MONEY HE HAS HAD IN *MONTHS*...

TARIM! ONLY IN BEDUIN WOULD A THIEF HIDE HIS PURSE IN A *BLOODY* MINE-SHAFT...

CEREBUS HOPES THE BOTTOM IS WHERE HE *THINKS* IT IS, THIS IS *ALREADY* MORE TROUBLE THAN AN EXTRA BIT OF GOLD IS *WORTH*...

DAMN! BAG OF GOLD SLIPPED OUT OF *CEREBUS'* HAND.

NOW... WHERE DID IT...

AN HOUR LATER

CEREBUS HAS TO HAVE THIS GOLD -- ALL OF IT DOWN TO THE VERY *LAST* COIN...

EARTH-PIGLET DREAMS ARE *MADE* OF THIS MUCH GOLD...

BUT HOW CAN CEREBUS *MOVE* IT ALL?

WHENEVER CEREBUS THINKS OF THE MERCHANT UP THERE, COMPLETELY *UNAWARE* OF...

OF COURSE! THE *MERCHANT* IS ASLEEP!

COCKROOACH.

AWWAAKEN -- COCKROACH!

SNFX?

I AM THE *SPIRIT* OF YOUR FATHER, *COCKROACH!*

YOU HAVE STRAYED FROM THE TRUE *PATH*, MY CHILD...

AND I HAVE COME FROM THE BEYOND TO COUNSEL YOU...

DO YOU NOT REMEMBER WHAT I TOLD YOU ABOUT *STEALING* WHEN YOU WERE A BOY!

OH, *YES*, FATHER!

YOU SAID IF I GOT *CAUGHT* YOU WOULD BEAT ME TO A PULP.

OH··OF COURSE...

THINK! THINK!

PRAISE TARIM! I AM HERE TO BRING YOU *THE WORD* -- THE WORD OF TARIM...

THE *WORD,* FATHER?

CONDOMINIUMS! TARIM HAS A CONDOMINIUM JUST FOR YOU! LUXURIOUS LIVING IN THE AFTERLIFE... *IF* YOU BELIEVE!

I *DO!* I *DO!!*

PRAISE TARIM!

BUT TARIM NEEDS *GOLD* FOR HIS GOOD WORKS AND *CONDOMINIUMS! LOTS* OF IT! *BARRELS* OF IT! *WALLS* FULL OF IT -- ALUMINUM SIDING DOESN'T GROW ON TREES! WILL *YOU* GIVE YOUR GOLD TO TARIM TODAY?

YOU ARE *FAST* BECOMING A *PRIZED* FOLLOWER! LET ME HEAR A '*PRAISE TARIM!*'

YES! YES!

PRAISE TARIM!

THE SPIRIT IS *REALLY* UPON YOU, *COCKROACH* MY BOY -- I'M GOING TO PUT YOUR NAME IN FOR BEACHFRONT PROPERTY AND A GARDENER

BUT RIGHT *NOW,* YOU'VE GOT TO GO GET A WAGON AND A TEAM OF HORSES SO WE CAN START RELOCATING TARIM'S *ASSETS!*

PRAISE TARIM! BUT WHERE AM I GOING TO GET A WAGON AT *THIS* TIME OF NIGHT?

STEAL ONE...

AND DON'T GET *CAUGHT* OR I'LL BEAT YOU TO A *PULP!*

CEREBUS RANKED THEM EASILY THE BEST THREE WEEKS OF HIS LIFE! EACH DAY, HE AND THE COCKROACH WOULD LOAD FIVE SACKS ON THE WAGON AND MOVE THEM TO A DRY WELL ABOUT A MILE OUTSIDE THE CITY. ONE TRIP A DAY SO NO SUSPICIONS WERE AROUSED. THEN THEY WENT ON TO NEARBY PEDRON

WHERE CEREBUS DRANK AND PLAYED *DIAMONDBACK* UNTIL THE SUN SET. IN A FEW WEEKS, HE COULD START MOVING THE GOLD TO IEST AND BUY HIS *OWN* TAVERN...

THIRTY YEARS!... COCKROACH-- MERCHANT...

OH-OH NOT *AGAIN*...

HOW MANY TIMES DOES YOUR FATHER HAVE TO TELL YOU?

TARIM DOESN'T WANT YOU TO THINK! TARIM ONLY WANTS YOUR GOLD...

NOW-- STOP-- THINKING!

PRAISE TARIM!

IF THAT HAPPENS ONE MORE TIME, CEREBUS IS GOING TO BE SELLING *COCKROACH FILETS* IN HIS NEW TAVERN

THERE'S THE CITY-GATES-- TRY TO NOT LOOK SUSPICIOUS, COCKROACH

THE COCKROACH!

...I...AM THE COCKROACH

uh -- COULD WE TALK ABOUT THIS *OUTSIDE* THE CITY GATES?

THE COCKROACH -- I -- STOLE ALL THAT GOLD AND NOW YOU, TOO ARE STEALING IT -- I'LL HAVE YOU ARRESTED! I, THE MERCHANT WILL USE THAT GOLD FOR TARIM! EVEN THE POOR WILL HAVE BEACH-FRONT CONDOMINIUMS!

KLB

IF CEREBUS ISN'T *CAREFUL*, HE'S GOING TO START A WHOLE NEW *RELIGION*...

MAYHAP MY BUSINESSMAN BUG HAS OUTLIVED HIS *USEFULNESS* AND IT IS TIME TO MOVE TARIM'S PRESENT ASSETS TO *IEST*...

CEREBUS CAN ALWAYS COME BACK FOR WHAT IS *LEFT* IN THE WALL IN A FEW *MONTHS*...

GOOD MORROW.

GOOD MORROW.

SOMETHING *WRONG* WITH YOUR FRIEND THERE?

HE SPENT LAST NIGHT BOBBING FOR FIGS IN A WINE VAT...

AND HE KEPT FORGETTING TO COME UP FOR *AIR*...

HARHAR! I KNOW THE FEELING WELL...

LOOK OUT!

PLOP!

YOU NEEDN'T *TROUBLE* YOURSELF.

ONE OF MY *MEN* WILL ASSIST HIM...

THE *COCKROACH HUNT* WOULD GIVE HIM AN EXTRA FEW SECONDS ONLY... THEY WOULD BE AFTER HIM NOW AS AN *ACCOMPLICE.* THE COCKROACH WOULD BE BUYING HIS FREEDOM RIGHT NOW WITH A WALL FULL OF GOLD

CEREBUS KNEW THE MILITARY GOVERNMENT WOULD BE DELIGHTED TO AT LAST BALANCE THEIR BUDGET.

FOR HIS PART, CEREBUS WOULD SEE THAT THEY DID NOT GET *ALL* THE GOLD...

SEVEN SACKS! A SUBSTANTIAL DROP FROM EIGHT FEET OF LOOT, BUT ENOUGH TO *GUARANTEE* CEREBUS ALE MONEY FOR THE DURATION OF THE SPRING...

ONE MORE MINUTE AND THE SOLDIERS WOULDN'T HAVE A *PRAYER* OF CATCHING HIM...

BUT EVEN AS HE LASHES THE SACKS INTO PLACE ON THE SADDLE...

...SEVEN MOUNTED SOLDIERS *THUNDER* TOWARD HIM IN A SWIRL OF DUST...

BRIEFLY, THE EARTH-PIG TURNS, *CONTEMPLATING* SOME REVENGE FOR THE LOSS OF HIS FORTUNE...

MAYHAP WHEN HE REACHES THE *HIGHLANDS...*

BUT FOR *NOW...*

...HE HAD TO REGAIN HIS LOST ADVANTAGE. ...AND *QUICKLY*...

TARIM!

ALREADY THEY ARE TOO CLOSE!

A SACRIFICE...

BUT THERE IS NO SACRIFICE TOO GREAT FOR KEEPING ONE'S FUR *INTACT*...

DEIDRE! COME WITH ME!

THE REST OF YOU GATHER UP THE GOLD!

CEREBUS HAD ONLY A FEW **SECONDS** TO ACT

THESE WERE NO LOCAL FARMERS IN SOLDIERS' CLOTHING. HE WOULD NEVER BEAT THEM TO THE HIGHLANDS.

HO!

DISMOUNT...

...BUT BE ON YOUR GUARD!

AYE! AND THREE MORE BAGS OF **GOLD**...

IT'S THE HORSE HE **STOLE**, ALL **RIGHT!**

HE MUST HAVE **JUMPED** RATHER THAN FACE A TRIAL AND **EXECUTION**...

I GUESS WE SHOULD HEAD BACK TO BEDUIN WITH THE GOLD...

GOLD? YOU MEAN THE THREE BAGS HE WAS HOLDING ONTO WHEN HE JUMPED?

HOLDING ONTO? BUT THEY'RE RIGHT THERE ON HIS...

OHO! I GET YOUR DRIFT...

MY BROTHER LIVES ABOUT A MILE FROM HERE... WE CAN GET HIM TO HIDE IT FOR US WHILE WE REPORT BACK...

CEREBUS IS SIMPLY GOING TO **HAVE** TO FIND A LESS **NERVE-WRACKING** WAY TO MAKE MONEY!

CEREBUS No. 12 (October - November, 1979)

As I said in the last introduction, I crammed a fair bit of the story into issue eleven. I think I wasn't much past page ten when I realized that I would just have to bring the character back so that all the little bits of funny business (or some of them anyway) that I had snipped from the finished story wouldn't go to waste.

Foremost among these was "Cerebus as Robin." Marshall Rodgers' ideas had gotten me thinking about The Batman as good material for an opera -- tragedy on a grandiose scale, emotions squirting all over the stage. The Robin part of the legend is especially evocative in this context. The morbid figure of the Batman, consumed by his own unhappiness, decked out in a black shroud, seeking only the lowest, vilest denizens of the great city, surrounded and immersed in a world devoid of pity and compassion. Until a small boy, suffering the same tragedy, touches something in this Darknight Wraith...

Heady heady stuff stuff, indeed indeed.

The nice thing about tragedy is that it is so closely linked to comedy. Again, the sequence practically wrote itself.

I remember this issue for a number of reasons. We moved my studio out of the apartment -- scratch that. We decided. Deni moved the studio out of the apartment. I went to visit Gene Day (I had to draw the issue, didn't I? Well, didn't I?). There is something about visiting Gene and working around him that brings out the absolute best in me. It is a strange feeling sitting somewhere else, working on a story. The pages don't look the same as they would if you were drawing at home. I don't know how I can say that for certain. But it is true. Even writing a story in a different place gives it a whole different quality. On the art side it contributed to there being more of a caricature quality to the drawing. About the only thing I regret on this issue is the decision to use duo-tone board (art board pre-printed with two tonal patterns, one light and one dark, each brought out by a separate developing fluid). It tended to make the artwork incredibly muddy in appearance. I had the story finished to the point where Cerebus is about to jump through the window, when a phone call from Deni came. The new studio was ready.

All the way back to Kitchener, I couldn't wait to see it. At long last, I was going to have a real, honest-to-gosh-bye-honey-I'm-going-to-work place of business.

When I finally saw it, my heart sank.

It looked like an indoor football field with a couple of pieces of furniture sticking up here and there. It was like someone was playing a bad joke on me. What was missing? Nothing. It was just a larger room that I had had. All those months of crying about my lack of space, my cramped quarters, my burning need for a little elbow room. Instant karma.

I did the page of Cerebus jumping through the window that night. Alone in a six-story office building built around the turn of the century. In the middle of a football field. No telephone. No T.V. No refrigerator. I had traded a stunning view of Queen Street and the lights of the city from a picture window on the fourteenth floor for a large chunk of glass embedded in unfinished cement looking out on rooftops that would've made Marshall Rogers or Frank Miller positively drool. Page two, panel one, Cruddy rooftops, Daredevil poised to leap.

Gaah.

That studio lasted until I was ready to begin issue seventeen. It gradually filled up. An armchair when we bought new furniture for the apartment, longer shelves, a standing drawing table. We put twenty-two nails on one wall in two rows of eleven and hung clips on them so I could have the pages in front of me while I was working on the issue.

The ending to this issue is a significant event in the aardvark's life. He fails again, miserably, in his attempt to get something for nothing. This time period of one failure after another very much reflected my view of my own life. Every time it looked like Cerebus might be starting to take off and become a going concern, something would happen to make us both feel that we were back at square one.

It wasn't that way of course. Just taking our progress over these four issues, our position became solider with each one. I got invited to the New York Con. Offers to do Cerebus stories were coming in from other people. I was learning more about what I was doing every time I did a page.

Cerebus No. 12 (cont'd)

Beduin was also the first city that I began to visualize extensively in my head. From issue eleven on, the background became less important to the artwork and became a more integral part of the story than ever before. For the most part, my enthusiasm for a realistic location stemmed from my brother-in-law Michael Loubert. I was beginning to rely on him more and more for authentic touches and insights into the workings of pre-industrial civilizations. In time, I would become over-bearing in my demands, looking for ideas from him that I should have been developing on my own. At this time, however, it was a substantial boost that the book needed to avoid a cosmetic feel to the cosmology.

If I was going to have to draw in the middle of a football field, I was to determined, at least, to draw the best book ever done in the middle of a football field.

IT WOULD HAVE TAKEN THE AVERAGE SAILOR FOUR HOURS TO PADDLE INTO BEDUIN. AN HOUR LATER, CEREBUS WAS WATCHING FOR THE LOOMING SHAPE OF THE *COCKROACH'S* FORMER RESIDENCE

BUT THEN THE AVERAGE SAILOR WOULD NOT HAVE HAD THE BENEFIT OF THE EARTH-PIG'S MOTIVATING FORCE....

FRUSTRATED GREED....

NO ONE IN *SIGHT*...CEREBUS PICKED A GOOD NIGHT

JUST AS CEREBUS *REMEMBERED*... THE STONE DOESN'T EXTEND ALL THE WAY TO THE BOTTOM...

AND THE WOOD LOOKS *ROTTEN* ENOUGH THAT...

SCRAMBLING ONTO THE NARROW LEDGE, CEREBUS COULD ALMOST *SMELL* HIS FORTUNE

A LITTLE *FORCE* SHOULD BRING A *CASCADE* OF GOLD INTO THE...

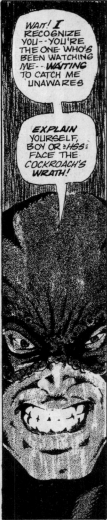

KILL YOUR PARENTS WILL THEY? DON'T YOU *WORRY* -- WE'LL GET REVENGE! *REVENGE* ≈HSSS≈ PUNCH 'EM INNA *FACE* KICK 'EM INNA *HEAD*...

WE'LL BE LIFE-LONG *PARTNERS* AND BOSOM *BUDDIES!* I'LL TEACH YOU EVERYTHING I *KNOW*...

THAT SHOULDN'T TAKE *LONG*...

ACTUALLY CEREBUS CAME TO *WARN* YOU OF A *PLOT* AGAINST YOU

PLOT?! HA! YOU HAVE SO MUCH TO *LEARN*... *EVERYONE* PLOTS AGAINST *THE COCKROACH*...THE COCKROACH KNOWS

NYAHHAHA HAHEEHEE HOOHAHAHA HAHAHENH

HSSS

BUT GO AHEAD, KID-- TELL YOUR *GUARDIAN* FRIEND, MENTOR AND *IDOL* ABOUT THIS ≈HEH≈ PLOT. I'LL BET YOU I KNOW *ALL* ABOUT IT

ELROD OF MELVINBONE PLANS TO COME AND *STEAL* YOUR *GOLD* TOMORROW

AHA

AHA? YOU MEAN YOU'VE *HEARD* OF HIM

HEARD OF HIM?-- HE'S COMING *TOMORROW* TO STEAL ALL MY *GOLD!*

OH--OF *COURSE*

CEREBUS MUST BE GETTING *ABSENT-MINDED* IN HIS OLD AGE...

NOW-- WHAT DO I DO ABOUT IT? I COULD--uh *NO*, THAT WOULDN'T WORK I COULD...I COULD...

uh...

WE COULD MOVE THE GOLD BEFORE HE *GETS* HERE ...

I'VE *GOT* IT!

WE'LL MOVE THE *GOLD* BEFORE HE GETS ...

YOUR ABILITY TO THINK THROUGH A *PROBLEM* IS *AMAZING* ...

HA-HA--THAT'S WHY EVERYONE ELSE IS *OUT THERE* AND THE COCKROACH IS *IN HERE!*

THERE WAS ONE CHANCE! *SIMULTANEOUS* WITH THE THOUGHT, CEREBUS PLUNGES INTO AN ALLEYWAY...

ONE WAY OR ANOTHER, THE COCKROACH WOULD HAVE TO BE PUT BACK IN HIS CELL...

...AND *SOON!*

THE *COCK AND BULL TAVERN!* IF HIS MEMORY WASN'T FAULTY AND HE COULD REACH THE *MEZZANINE* IN TIME...

SORRY --WE'RE...

AAAK

OUT OF MY WAY, *DOLT!!*

YOU CAN'T--I'LL CALL THE *WATCH!*

...THINKS HE CAN CATCH *CEREBUS* ...

HE'S WELCOME TO TRY...

IF THERE'S A SOLDIER IN *BEDUIN* ...

TARIM! NO SIGN OF HIM ON THE *RIVER* ...

CEREBUS CAN ONLY HOPE HE'S *DIRECTLY UNDER* THE...

CEREBUS IS JUST GOING TO LET THE *COOTIE* MAKE MINCE-MEAT OUT OF HIM...

CEREBUS ALREADY KNOWS ELROD WOULD BE HARD-PRESSED TO BEAT AN *EGG* *

* SEE CEREBUS #4

REVENGE HSSS

STAND WHERE YOU ARE, *MORTAL!*

FOR I AM THE *COCKROACH* AND...

COCKROACH? PLEASED TO MEET YOU, SON! NAME'S ELROD, ACCENT ON THE 'EL'

SAY-- PURPLE IS YOUR COLOUR, *BOY!* WHAT-- I SAY--WHAT'S YOUR LINE OF WORK?

I DEDICATE MYSELF *DAILY* TO FACING THE *CRIMINAL ELEMENT* ON THEIR OWN TERRITORY IN *MORTAL COMBAT*

SORT OF A COMBINATION SOCIAL WORKER AND *HOODLUM,* EH? *!!*

YOUR UNIFORM'S ALL *WRONG,* SON...

MY... UNIFORM?

YOUR *HEADGEAR,* SON...IT'S ABOUT AS USEFUL AS A *BOREALAN* AT A *BANQUET!*

IMPRACTICAL, THAT IS

CEREBUS HAD **ALREADY** INVESTED THE BETTER HALF OF TWO MONTHS IN THE GOLD! IF THE FATES DEMANDED THAT HE GET NO MORE THAN A BOAT-LOAD, SO **BE** IT, BUT NO SECOND-RATE SOLDIERS WERE GOING TO GET IN HIS ...

...WAY.

TWANG

THAK!

HE WOULD HEAD FOR ONE OF THE SMALLER TOWNS BORDERING BEDUIN AND BUY THE *TAVERN* HE HAD BEEN THINKING ABOUT...

SOME DAY-- I SAY, SOME *DAY*, SON, WE'RE GOING TO HAVE TO HAVE A *LONG* TALK...

AND YOU CAN EXPLAIN WHAT IN THE HECK JUST *HAPPENED* HERE...

AS HE DRIFTS OUT OF THE TUNNEL, CEREBUS LOOKS UP TO SEE THE SUN *RISING*...

'THE LONG BEDUIN NIGHT WAS OVER

...AND THE GOLD WAS HIS...

WITH THE SUN COMES A WAVE OF *EXULTATION* AND A STRANGE NEW SENSE OF OPTIMISM...

LET THEM SEND MORE SOLDIERS -- A WHOLE *ARMY!* HE WOULD FIGHT *THEM* OFF, TOO -- THE-GOLD-WAS-HIS!!

A BOATFUL OF IT!!

ABRUPTLY, CEREBUS' WORLD SHATTERS AND QUICKLY *REFORMS* AS A MONTAGE OF IMAGES -- MURKY WATER, SPLINTERED TIMBERS AND AN ELUSIVE TWINKLING VANISHING BELOW HIM...

CEREBUS' HEAD BREAKS THE SURFACE AND HE GULPS LUNGS-FUL OF *AIR* -- AIR THAT SOMEHOW NO LONGER SMELLED AS SWEET AS IT HAD BARE MOMENTS BEFORE...

HE SWIMS TO THE SHATTERED FRAME OF THE BOAT! HIS INTENTION WAS TO ESCAPE BEFORE THE SOLDIERS *AWOKE*

THERE WAS NO TIME FOR REGRET OR SELF-RECRIMINATION...

IF ANYTHING, HE IS GRATEFUL THAT THE WEATHER IS WARM AND THE CURRENT SWIFT...

WITH A MINIMUM OF EFFORT HE WOULD BE OUTSIDE OF BEDUIN'S WALLS WITHIN THE HOUR IN SEARCH OF SHELTER FOOD AND ALE

"ALL THINGS CONSIDERED," MUSES THE EARTH-PIG...

"IT'S BEEN ONE HELL OF A LOUSY *TWENTY-SEVENTH* BIRTHDAY..."

"WHAT HAPPENED BETWEEN ISSUES TWENTY AND TWENTY-ONE"

"How did you meet Gene Day?"

It's one of those questions with a long answer; like "Why an aardvark?"

So here goes the Reader's Digest version.

I was at Now & Then Books in 1973 when Vince Marchesano (watch for Bludd the Barbarian from Charlton Bullseye) was there and I happened to be looking over his shoulder when he was paging through his address book. He had the address and phone number of Al Hewetson in St. Catharines who, at the time, was the editor for the Skywald line of Horror-mood magazines. We were organizing the second Southern Ontario Panel Art Festival (SOPAF) to be held at the store later that summer, so I contacted Mr. Hewetson, and also asked if we could do an interview with him for the second issue of the Now and Then Times, an interview fanzine that we did two annual issues of. He agreed and suggested that we also contact one of his writers, Augustine Funnell, who lived in a small town near Kingston (we'll call it Mayberry, so that Gene doesn't get a thousand people showing up at his door). Gus came to the Festival and we did an interview with him for Comic Art News and Reviews (CANAR), a bi-monthly fanzine I did a lot of work for, published and edited by John Balge. Six months later I got a letter from a friend of his, Gene Day, who mentioned that he was publishing a fanzine called Dark Fantasy that featured fiction and illustrations by amateur and semi-professional writers and artists. He asked me to submit some illustrations. I sent him four or five of the sleaziest, worst-rendered, unreproduceable pen and ink drawings that have ever been done anywhere and by anyone. And he accepted them. We were friends for life.

We wrote voluminous letters back and forth loaded with tips on markets we had heard about for drawings. This guy is paying $12 a picture, but he keeps the original and all rights. This one's paying $20, but it has to look like Steve Fabian. I finally went up to see him in June of 1974. He was living in a few rooms upstairs from Gus Funnell and had just cracked his first "pro" market, doing single illustrations for Skywald. (as had I, having sold my first and only story to Al Hewetson; "Cry of the White Wolf"). His studio floored me. Everywhere you looked, there were drawings. Single illustrations, daily strips, comic book stories, editorial cartoons, sketches, spot illos. And he wasn't living at home with his parents.

The next year, I visited again, this time for a week. I helped him on some backgrounds for Project One, a comic book he had sold to George Breo's Windy City Publishing in Chicago. We also drew a three page horror strip for one of the Charlton horror books called "Grave-digger's Banquet" from a script of mine Al Hewetson had rejected. It was rejected. At the same time, he was working on two stories for ORB magazine, as well as a number of illustrations for the Robert E. Howard fanzines that were glutting the market at the time.

The next year, newly appointed senior editor of Orb, I was back in Mayberry, typing scripts and doing some work myself for them. This time I stayed a month, having talked Harry Kremer into publishing Oktoberfest Comics as a one-shot with art by Gene and me.

The most significant visit though, was the time Gene came to Kitchener after a convention in the hinterland somewhere near Toronto and stayed at my parent's place. Having stripped Now and Then Books to the bare walls (comicshop owners should offer Gene all-expense paid trips to come and see them), Gene and I were at the train station ready to say good-bye. Conversationaly, he asked me what I had out in the mail at the moment. What stuff I was waiting to hear back on.

Nothing.

It was then, after nearly four years of seeing Gene and his staggering output, that it finally sunk in. That's why he was living on his own, paying rent and building a name for himself in the field. I hadn't done anything. We still joke a lot about that day. Gene ready to leave, and faced with this guy foaming at the mouth and calling himself every name in the book. I was a no-good, lazy, half-assed, leech. Here were my parents, willing to back me to the hilt, making my life as easy as possible and what was I doing? Nothing! Farting around! Jacking off! Pissing it away! The phraseology got even more colourful. I was a scum, a no-good ungrateful moron waiting for someone to hand him the world on a silver platter. When Gene got on the train, I managed to interrupt myself (useless, half-witted) long enough to say goodbye. I went home and over the next six months I produced. Lord, how I produced -- illustrations, stories, full pagers, spot illos, cartoons, caricatures, covers. Six months later I moved out of home and never went back, except to visit.

People tend to be amazed that I manage to produce a twenty page comic book once a month. In some cases, "amazed" doesn't half

What Happened .... (cont'd)

describe their reaction. It is Gene Day who is responsible for that ability in me. The fact that he was the only artist I knew personally who had made the jump from amateur to semi-professional to professional imprinted his path on my own ambitions. If he were to add up every dollar he has been cheated out of, over the course of his many years in the business (I don't think he'd mind me saying this) he'd be extremely wealthy today. I learned that sense of risk from Gene. There are people out there who'll take you for every penny, and there is, unfortunately, no way for the beginning artist to avoid them. It is part and parcel of freelancing to new and unproven companies. Having seen all that Gene went through, just by virtue of the size of his output and the number of companies he worked for, I was prepared when something happened. Don't take it personally. Do something else and sell it.

I think of Gene whenever someone comes up to me at a convention, or writes a letter, asking how to get into the business. How to stop doing art for free and start doing it for money. I see him hunched over a drawing board (it's hard to picture Gene any other way) leaning back from time to time, assessing. Always assessing. Sizing up a market. Comparing editors. Praising a magazine's cover design. Trying to figure a new means of distribution, another place to submit material. The man is a walking encyclopedia of Techniques for the Ambitious Artist.

On top of all that, he has always crushed me with his sense of black. Where to put it. How much. He leaves the cap off his ink so it will get thicker. There is nothing even remotely resembling a washed out black on a Gene Day original. And he is so **clean!** Look at the corners of a Gene Day panel. They're corners! Square -- the corners come to a point. Look at the corners of a Dave Sim panel (on second thought **don't** look at the corners of a Dave Sim panel). I get embarrassed when I think of the things I have swiped from Gene's style. The broken pen lines to indicate the sides of trees, shadow patterns on faces, panel layouts, page designs. I get embarrassed when I see his photograph files. Trains, animals, buildings, backgrounds, architecture, statues. I always dreaded the day that Gene would get a book to pencil at Marvel. Anyone else in the business, I can handle seeing what they do. Objective, y'know. Nice building there. Like the way you caught that face. I look at the pages to Kung-Fu 110 in pencil and part of me starts screaming. "Look! Look! That's what you're supposed to be doing!

Drawing, you asshole. Exterior views of the Regency right down to the shadows of the pupils on the gargoyles' eyes. Shingles, window panes, swirling sculpture, foregrounds and backgrounds and middle distance." Split panels, sequences, compositions, designs. When you compliment me on using all that stuff in my stories, I can tell you in all honesty that it's there because I have to keep up with that son of a bitch. And every time I make it -- EVERY TIME I KNOW THAT THIS _TIME I've managed to come up with a series of figures to animate a motion EVERY TIME I've taken the camera to such an extreme worm's eye view of the side of a building that the perspective looks like a squat pyramid EVERY TIME I've drawn up a page where you start reading the panel on the girl's right shoulder that follows into a tracking shot down her stomach and into the background where it becomes outlined by the silhouette of the flashback sequence given a dream-like quality by the sheet of white tone overtop, EVERY TIME I go to Mayberry (Hey, Goober. Hey, Gene) that bastard has drawn something that absolutely puts it to shame.

"So what d'ya think?"

I'd like to kick yer damn teeth down yer talented throat.

"It's nice. Real good."

"I thought I'd come in through here with some spatter, to sort of make the face come out more."

The face is sitting there on the page crackling with black energy.

"I don't think it needs it."

"This is a pencilled page I've been working on. Finishing up one night and I thought I'd get a start on it."

When I finish for the night, it's all I can do to keep from ripping open the elevator doors and dragging the thing up by hand. Lemme outta here!

Gene's been doing a few paintings lately.

Gene's been doing some sketches on this ...

Gene's been throwing this together ...

Gene thought he'd do a sample this ...

Gene thought he'd do a try at this ...

It is this driving ambition, incredible speed, addiction to accuracy and complete and utter dissatisfaction with the way he draws that has brought Gene to the prominence he has today as one of Marvel's handful of top-flight pencillers.

At least I hope it's that.

Because if it comes from drinking all that coffee and smoking all those cigarettes, I haven't got a prayer of keeping up with him.

What Happened Between Issues
twenty & twenty·one

SECONDS AFTER WENDA HAS DEPARTED, THE DOOR TO HER APARTMENT SWINGS OPEN. PADDING SOUND-LESSLY INTO THE ROOM, THE SLIGHT FIGURE MOVES SWIFTLY, UNROLLING A LARGE CLOTH SACK. GLANCING NERVOUSLY OUT THE WINDOW, HE SETS TO WORK...

HE KNOWS THE RISK INVOLVED IN TAKING THE AARDVARK. HIS ORDERS HAD BEEN TO WATCH THE APARTMENT AND TO NOTE ANY ARRIVALS OR DEPARTURES. THE REALIZATION THAT THE AARDVARK WAS ALONE AND STILL UNCONSCIOUS HAD PROVED TOO GREAT A TEMPTATION

HIS HEART POUNDS AS A DOZEN SECONDS TICK BY. "FOUR THOUSAND CROWNS FOR THE AARDVARK ALIVE." SO MUCH MONEY. AT LAST HE WOULD BE ABLE TO LEAVE THE INTRIGUE AND SKULLDUGGERY OF TOGITH BEHIND. AN OPPORTUNITY LIKE THIS CAME ONLY ONCE IN A GREAT WHILE. LET THE OTHERS DO AS THEY WERE TOLD FOR A HANDFUL OF COPPER BITS... G'EVAN WAS SMARTER THAN ALL OF THEM. SMARTER THAN TEPIN -- SMARTER THAN MEIGRE, SMARTER, EVEN, THAN....

STRANGIS WATCHES THE AARDVARK VANISH INTO THE RED HORN TAVERN. HE COULDN'T RISK AN ABDUCTION IN A PUBLIC PLACE...
HE WOULD JUST HAVE TO WAIT FOR THE BEAST TO EMERGE AND THEN FOLLOW HIM.
    FOR HIS PART, CEREBUS FEELS AN OVERWHELMING NEED FOR A DRINK. THE SIDEWALK SEEMS TO BUCKLE AND TWIST
UNDER HIS FEET AS HE WEAVES TOWARD THE TAVERN. HE IS UNAWARE THAT THE DRUGS ADMINISTERED TO HIM BY PERCE
AND WENDA ARE ACTIVATED BY ALCOHOL.

BEFORE HE HAS DOWNED HALF A GLASS OF ALE, HIS CONDITION BEGINS TO WORSEN. HIS ARMS AND LEGS FEEL LIKE LEAD
WEIGHTS AND HIS EYES REFUSE TO FOCUS FOR MORE THAN A FEW SECONDS AT A TIME...

ATTEMPTING TO LEAVE, HE MISTAKENLY USES THE REAR EXIT, NOT REALIZING THAT HE HAS JUST SAVED HIMSELF FROM THE
CLUTCHES OF THE MURDEROUS MR. STRANGIS. BY THE TIME HIS SNOUT STRIKES THE PAVEMENT, HE IS UNCONSCIOUS.

BY PROCLAMATION OF HIS HOLINESS, FREAK SHOWS WERE NOT PERMITTED IN IEST, AND SO IT IS THAT CEREBUS, COMATOSE BUT STILL BREATHING, SPENDS THE NEXT TWO WEEKS TOURING THE SURROUNDING TOWNS AND VILLAGES. IT IS NOT UNTIL THE SHOW REACHES THE LARGER TOWN OF HARPENGATE THAT HE IS ONCE AGAIN RECOGNIZED...

HE IS B'REN KAEL, EXECUTIVE ASSISTANT TO THE REEVE OF HARPENGATE, ON A ROUTINE INSPECTION VISIT TO THE FREAK SHOW. FOR THE NEXT TWO DAYS, HE NEGOTIATES WITH THE OWNER TO PURCHASE THE AARDVARK, FEARING THAT AT ANY MOMENT ANOTHER MIDDLE-LEVEL BUREAUCRAT MIGHT MAKE THE SAME DISCOVERY. SEVERAL TIMES A DEAL IS ALMOST STRUCK ONLY TO BE NEGATED BY THE OWNER. ONE HUNDRED CROWNS. TWO HUNDRED. FIVE. EIGHT. ONE THOUSAND. FINALLY, B'REN SIGNS A BANK DRAUGHT THAT VIRTUALLY DRAINS HIS SAVINGS TO THE LAST HALF-BIT...

THE OWNER HAD DECIDED HE COULD LIVE WITH A MODEST EIGHT THOUSAND PER CENT PROFIT MARGIN.

TIME WAS THE ENEMY, NOW. HE HAD BEEN IN THE ORGANIZATION LONG ENOUGH TO KNOW THAT THERE WERE PROBABLY A DOZEN AGENTS CONVERGING ON EVERY TOWN AROUND IEST WITH A SINGLE PURPOSE: "FIND THE AARDVARK AND BRING HIM IN ALIVE."

HE STICKS TO THE LESS-TRAVELLED ROADS AND PRAYS THAT HE HAS AT LEAST A TWO HOUR HEAD START...

KNOCK

KNOCK
KNOCK   KNOCK

WHO IS IT?

"THE EYE ASCENDS"

"AND SEES THE DAWN"

"OF A NEW AGE"

SIR GERRIK...

I--I HAVE SOMETHING TO SELL...

REALLY.

IN THAT CASE, PERHAPS YOU SHOULD COME IN AND TELL ME ABOUT IT...

I... HAVE THE AARDVARK...

IT WAS JUST BY CHANCE -- I STUMBLED UPON HIM!

I....

YOU SEE MY PROBLEM?

I HAD TO FIND SOMEONE I COULD TRUST-- WHO WOULDN'T THINK I WAS TRYING TO THREATEN THEIR POSITION

I APPRECIATE YOUR HONESTY, B'REN. MIGHT I ASK HOW MUCH YOU WOULD SELL HIM FOR?

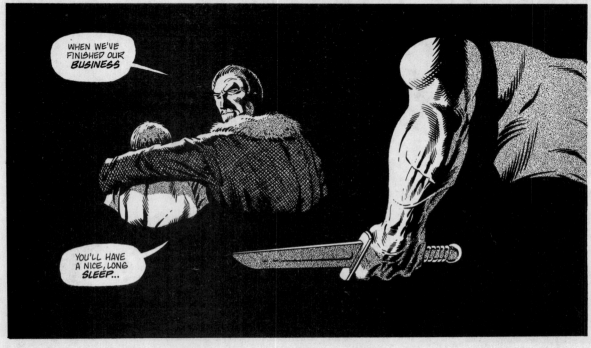

IT WAS CLUMSY... LETTING STRANGIS GET THAT CLOSE. I THOUGHT WE HAD LOST HIM FOR GOOD...

STRANGIS IS THE LEAST OF OUR WORRIES, NOW.

HIS BREATHING IS TOO SHALLOW. THE PULSE IS WEAK. WE CAN'T AFFORD THE RISK OF DRUGGING HIM AGAIN...

AND HE'S ALREADY STARTED TO REGAIN CONSCIOUSNESS

IF HE DOES, HE'LL BE OFF TO REJOIN GUDRE AND THAT WILL BE THE END OF HIM...

WE'LL JUST HAVE TO DRUG HIM ANYWAY ...

AND I'M TELLING YOU THAT HE STANDS A BETTER CHANCE WITH THE T'SITANS THAN HE DOES GETTING DRUGGED...

JUDGING THE RAPID RATE OF HIS RECOVERY, WE'RE GOING TO HAVE TO FIGURE OUT WHAT TO DO...

...SOON! IT'S A MATTER OF HOURS --MAYHAP A *DAY*, AT BEST.

SO *LET* HIM RECOVER! WE CAN TIE HIM DOWN, AND WHEN HE'S FULLY AWAKE...

...WE CAN DRUG HIM AGAIN, SAFELY!

WE HAVE NO WAY OF KNOWING HOW MUCH OF THE DRUG IS STILL IN HIS *SYSTEM*...

AND IF HE'S CONSUMED ANY ALCOHOL, WHICH HE LIKELY HAS, EVEN A HALF-GRAIN COULD KILL HIM...

I DO HAVE A SUGGESTION... IF I TAKE HIM BACK TO BEDUIN WITH ME, I CAN USE MY FORGED PAPERS TO GET HIM *INSIDE*. HE'LL HAVE TO STAY UNTIL THE BAN ON TRAVEL IS *LIFTED*...

BY THAT TIME, GUDRE'S TROOPS WILL HAVE BEEN DECIMATED BY LORD GORCE...

AND MAYBE OUR LITTLE FRIEND HERE WILL LEARN A VALUABLE LESSON...

I WOULD, HOWEVER, HAVE TO LEAVE *IMMEDIATELY* ...